Questions You'll Wish You Asked Yourself

A Journal to Understand Your Past,
Feel Peace in the Present,
& Create the Future You Want

Questions You'll Wish You Asked Yourself

A Journal to Understand Your Past,
Feel Peace in the Present,
& Create the Future You Want

MELISSA PENNEL

Follow Your Fire Publishing
Sacramento, CA.

Melissa Pennel / Follow Your Fire Publishing
FollowYourFireCoaching.com
Sacramento, CA.

THE LETTERS OF EMILY DICKINSON, edited by Thomas H. Johnson, Associate Editor, Theodora Ward, Cambridge, Mass.: The Belknap Press of Harvard University Press, Copyright © 1958 by the President and Fellows of Harvard College. Copyright © renewed 1986 by the President and Fellows of Harvard College. Copyright © 1914, 1924, 1932, 1942 by Martha Dickinson Bianchi. Copyright © 1952 by Alfred Leete Hampson. Copyright © 1960 by Mary L. Hampson. Used by permission. All rights reserved.

Ordering Information:
Quantity sales: Special discounts are available on quantity purchases by corporations, associations, and others. For details, contact the publisher at the address above.

Questions You'll Wish You Asked Yourself: A Journal to Understand Your Past, Feel Peace in the Present, & Create the Future You Want, Melissa Pennel —1st ed.
This journal is not a substitute or replacement for professional help. See mental health resources on page 156 for additional support.

Paperback ISBN: 978-1-956446-23-4
Hardcover ISBN: 978-1-956446-24-1

Book design by Attila Orosz

This journal belongs to:

If found please contact at:

...I am out with lanterns, looking for myself.

~ Emily Dickinson ~

Contents

Introduction 1

How to Use This Journal 3

Your Younger Self 7

Your Family 31

On Work 45

Your Relationships 57

Something Bigger 75

Knowing Yourself Better 81

Identifying Your Values 99

Navigating Tough Moments 103

Your Future Self 123

Questions for Every Day 139

Questions for the Liminal Space 145

Love Notes from Myself *(Extra Journaling Pages)* 149

Mental Health Resources 156

Living Questions, Breathing Answers Virtual Group 157

About the Author 158

The Questions You'll Wish You Asked Series:

A Time Capsule Journal for Mothers and Daughters
A Time Capsule Journal for Mothers and Sons
A Time Capsule Journal for Fathers and Daughters
A Time Capsule Journal for Fathers and Sons
A Time Capsule Journal for Parents and Children
A Time Capsule Journal for Grandmothers and Grandchildren
A Time Capsule Journal for Grandfathers and Grandchildren
A Time Capsule Journal for Grandparents and Grandchildren
A Time Capsule Journal for Treasured Mentors & Trusted Guides

The Motherless Mother's Journal Series

Learn more at

FOLLOWYOURFIRECOACHING.COM

This journal is dedicated to your inner child, inner elder, and the You that writes answers in the present moment. May they heal, laugh, and dance together within these pages.

Introduction

When I published the first Questions You'll Wish You Asked journal, I actually meant to write a different book: one about how to find your inner guide. It's something I was already helping people do in my work as a life coach and writer, so it "made sense."

But as the pandemic of 2020 raged, wildfires burned across my state, and I struggled to parent a toddler while pregnant with my second, I was having trouble accessing my own inner guide—let alone helping someone else do it. My chronic morning sickness mixed with the loneliness of how small my life had become, and it all revealed a fresh grief for my mother, who had died years before. *What if she were still here?* I'd think, then feel foolish. She wasn't, and I was arguing with reality... but if she were, what would I ask her about how to get through? From this place another idea kept nudging me: all the questions I wish I'd asked her before she passed away, and answers about life I wanted to write down for my own daughters. Writing and answering these questions seemed to be a salve, so I began doing so in moments of energy. Each time I felt a bit better, so I kept doing it.

I eventually scrapped my first idea and decided to publish the Questions You'll Wish You Asked: A Time Capsule Journal for Mothers and Daughters. I was unsure if anyone else would fill it out, and then it surprised me by becoming a bestseller. I watched in awe as messages and reviews poured in from people I'd never met, some sharing their experience with the journal, others saying they'd given it to a dying loved one, and many asking for more versions, which I eventually created for every family relationship. But as these journals made their way around the world, it became apparent that something else was happening, too... something independent of the connection between the family members sharing the journal.

"I feel like answering these questions is helping me," one commenter said. "They're reminding me where I've been, how impermanent all of this, and how I'll want to have lived at the end of my life."

The family journals were meant to bridge generational gaps and sow awareness of life's impermanence, and as I read these messages I saw that those things were also needed within another relationship... the one with ourselves. The Questions You'll Wish You Asked Yourself journal does exactly that: bridge space between the people we used to be, those we might have been, and those we are. It sows compassion and understanding throughout the inner nesting doll of selves, helps us identify what we value and want to keep centered, and reminds us of life's impermanence—not to incite panic or anxiety, things we get enough of in our achievement-oriented culture... but to make all of this life more sacred and important. To identify the You beneath the various selves, guiding you back to center when you've been caught up in the outer current.

On the pages that follow, you'll journey along the dusty shelves of your own past, picking up and examining fossilized memories only to find their still-beating heart within your own. You'll step into a time machine and meet your inner elder, asking them "how might we want to have lived?" You'll return not with a frantic to-do list, but with the guidance only a wiser version of *you* can provide.

You'll explore your shadow and your light, coming back to the awareness that all of these parts orbit a deeper and more knowing Self.

I'm glad you're holding it and believe this book found you for a reason. Welcome.

How to Use This Journal

✧ You can fill the journal out chronologically or open it intuitively when you want to move some energy. Remember that you don't need to wait for a certain age, amount of experience, or spark of insight to begin writing. The action of writing itself can untangle our thoughts and give way to a deeper, wiser, part... if we just begin.

✧ Return to these questions again and again. You'll find a different perspective each time you ask, and you can continue writing in additional notebooks once the journal pages fill. Since your initial answers are only the beginning, get messy and imperfect within this journal space.

✧ Consider combining these questions with other tools: Bring one into your meditation, ask a question before taking a long walk, or invite one into a breathwork practice. If you've never tried breathwork, it's a great tool for those of us who tend to live in our heads—people who have a lot of self-knowledge but still circle the same issues again and again. Breath can integrate real healing and grounding by going beneath conscious thought (what we "know") and releasing deeper stories lodged in our cells (what our bodies "know."). If you have no idea how to do it, don't worry—I created simple, self-guided, free to access breathwork tracks to deepen your experience with this journal, and links to access them are spread throughout the sections.

✧ While definitely not required, the links to free guided meditations and breathwork practices throughout this journal are designed to deepen your experience. You're also invited to join the Living Questions & Breathing Answers group at *Followyourfirecoaching.com/yourself* where you can attend group journaling sessions, live breathwork ceremonies, and access a library of additional meditation and breathwork tracks. **But remember, you don't need to do "all the things." Just writing in this journal is enough; simply reading a question and taking it into the day ahead can also be enough.** Let whatever feels right for you be the guide.

✧ There is a section at the end filled with questions for every day. You don't need to ask every question every day, but they are a great place to head before diving into your personal morning practice, journaling, or before turning in at night.

✧ The "Love Notes From Myself" section is filled with blank pages—flip to it if you want to elaborate further on an answer, have a spark of insight after a meditation, or simply want to write something down to revisit.

✧ If as you complete this journal it ever feels like "too much," please honor that signal—remember that it's always okay to ask for professional support, even when things are just feeling tricky. It can even deepen your practice with this journal to go through it with a trained professional. See the mental health resources on page 156 for a place to start.

Within these pages you'll find over 100 prompts that invite you to a liminal space of living the questions and "not needing to know" all the answers. But in diving into that space, you'll find a deeper you that has the exact medicine, healing, and answers that you're searching for. Your inner guide, if you will—which of course feels like an auspicious journey back to the original book I meant to write.

I suspect my own inner guide was first asking me to trust her before I tried to lead anyone else to find theirs, or maybe my mom was somehow reaching through time to deliver what I most needed... a project for the world that got me out of my head and into my heart. Whatever the reason, this longer journey means I've now got additional tools to lay at your feet, and the humility of a deeper inner journey myself. I join you today as a fellow explorer on this path of living the questions—may they open a space within where there is no "right" version of your past, your future, or your life. May they guide you to what is most true, beautiful, and present right here, right now...

You.

With love,
Melissa Pennel
June 2023

Your Younger Self

Why reflect on the past? Why concern ourselves with a holiday memory from decades ago, our favorite song at the age of ten, or what was on the walls at our grandmother's house?

It might seem counterintuitive, but reflecting on the past can help us construct a narrative of our lives—one that explains how we became who we are. It can also be an opportunity to befriend and heal the younger selves that still live within us: ages that seem far away until we catch a whiff of our child's crayons and remember sitting on the kindergarten rug ourselves, or we have an outsized reaction to something connected to a teenage wound and find ourselves thinking, *"what just happened?"*

The following pages contain prompts about your history and younger selves. Approach them with an open mind: things you thought were long forgotten may be just below the surface, or a familiar memory might land differently from your present-age.

Within us we contain all the ages we've ever been, and all of those former selves are here and ready to be revisited, better understood, and healed. They might just be waiting for the right question.

A guided meditation and breathwork track to accompany this section can be found at FollowYourFireCoaching.com/yourself

What is your earliest memory? ....

....

....

....

....

....

....

....

....

....

....

....

Imagine finding a short note to the future from your eight-year-old self. What questions, advice, or hopes would you have for your future self? ....

....

....

....

....

....

....

....

....

....

....

....

Do you know how your parents chose your name? Does it have a special meaning? If you haven't looked it up before, do so now. Does anything you found feel important?

....
....
....
....
....
....
....

Can you remember your childhood bedroom? Can you describe the way it looked, the things you did there, how it felt to be within it? ....

....
....
....
....
....
....

Do you have a favorite summer memory? What made this summer special?...

....
....
....
....
....
....
....

Did you have any irrational childhood fears? Do you remember how you got over them?....................................

....

....

....

....

....

....

....

....

....

In reflecting on this fear, do you see any connections to adulthood? If you could comfort that child version of you, what would you say?...

....

....

....

....

....

....

....

....

....

....

....

....

Did you have a secret hiding place as a child? Where was it? ....

....

....

....

....

....

....

....

....

....

Is there a place you go (or can go) now that reminds you of this feeling of safety? Maybe it's a hammock in your backyard, a botanical garden you love visiting, or a cave-like enclave on a trail you frequent. Where do you feel protected, held, and safe?

....

....

....

....

....

....

....

....

....

....

....

....

....

What are some favorite holiday memories? Who was present, what did you do, and how did you feel during these times?

....
....
....
....
....
....
....
....
....
....
....

Did you have a childhood best friend? What are some dear memories you shared? ....

....
....
....
....
....
....
....
....
....
....
....
....
....

What was your favorite game to play as a kid? What did you love about it?

....

....

....

....

....

....

....

....

....

....

Did you have any childhood pets? What do you remember about them?

....

....

....

....

....

....

....

....

....

....

....

....

What did you most struggle with as a child? ....

....

....

....

....

....

....

....

....

....

....

....

If you could comfort that inner child today, what would
you say? ....

....

....

....

....

....

....

....

....

....

....

....

....

Who did you look up to as a child, and why? How does that admiration reveal what was important to you?

....

....

....

....

....

....

....

....

....

....

....

....

....

....

....

....

....

....

....

....

....

....

....

....

If they're still around, would you consider reaching out to them to share how they impacted you?

What big differences do you see about how your generation was raised versus today's generation? What was better back then, and what was more difficult? ....

....

....

....

....

....

....

....

....

....

....

What was a dream you had as a child? Do you see any relationship between those dreams and the adult you became?

....

....

....

....

....

....

....

....

....

....

....

....

....

Was there a trip you took as a child that stands out to you? What made it special? ....

....

....

....

....

....

....

....

....

....

....

What type of music did your parents listen to? Did you like it? Consider making a playlist and writing to it.

....

....

....

....

....

....

....

....

....

....

....

....

What were some of your favorite songs, movies, and books from childhood? ....

....

....

....

....

....

....

....

....

....

Look up the top ten songs from the year you were ten years old and play a few. What memories arise as you listen?

....

....

....

....

....

....

....

....

....

....

....

....

If you could change one thing about your childhood, what would it be? How do you think that aspect of your upbringing made you who you are today? ....

....

....

....

....

....

....

....

....

....

....

....

....

....

....

....

....

....

....

....

....

....

....

....

....

....

Where did you feel most safe as a kid? ....
....
....
....
....
....
....
....
....
....
....
....
....
....
....
....
....
....
....
....
....
....
....
....

After writing about this moment, close your eyes and bring it to mind. Remember the sounds, smells, or people present. Let it anchor you and come back to it when needed.

What are your siblings' names? Did you get along? If you were an only child, did you ever wish for siblings?

....
....
....
....
....
....
....
....
....
....
....

What are the biggest similarities between your current self and your ten year old self? What are the biggest differences?

....
....
....
....
....
....
....
....
....
....
....
....
....

If your teen years were a movie, what was the theme? Who were the main characters? Was there a sweetheart or a villain? (An idea: make a soundtrack from your teen years and listen along as you write.) ....

....

....

....

....

....

....

....

....

....

....

....

....

....

....

....

....

....

....

....

....

....

....

....

Did you play the villain in anyone else's story? What happened?

....
....
....
....
....
....
....
....
....
....
....

What would you say to that version of yourself today? (How can you have compassion toward that version of yourself? What did they not yet know?) ....

....
....
....
....
....
....
....
....
....
....
....
....
....
....

Did you ever get in really big trouble as a teen? What were the consequences? ....

....

....

....

....

....

....

How would you have spent any money that you had back then? ....

....

....

....

....

....

....

Did you make any special accomplishments as a teen? Do they say anything about who you later became?

....

....

....

....

....

....

....

....

What did you most struggle with as a teen? ....

....

....

....

....

....

....

....

....

....

....

....

If you could comfort that version of yourself, what would
you say? ....

....

....

....

....

....

....

....

....

....

....

....

Is there any part of your body that made you self-conscious when you were young, but you now appreciate?

....

....

....

....

....

....

....

....

....

....

....

Is there anything you were self-conscious about in general when you were young, but now appreciate? ....

....

....

....

....

....

....

....

....

....

....

....

....

....

What did you do for fun as a teen? ....

....

....

....

....

....

....

....

....

....

....

....

Did you feel like you fit in as a teenager? Why or why not?

....

....

....

....

....

....

....

....

....

....

....

....

If you could hand your eighteen-year-old self a short note to take forward into the future, what would it say? ....

....

....

....

....

....

....

....

....

....

....

....

....

....

....

....

....

....

....

....

....

....

....

....

....

....

If your eighteen-year-old self were to give *you* (their future self) a note of advice or hope, what do you think it would have said? ....

....

....

....

....

....

....

....

....

....

....

....

....

....

....

....

....

....

....

....

....

....

....

....

....

What new perspective do you have after writing about your younger selves? Are there any behaviors or experiences you now see with a different lens, or with more understanding?

....

....

....

....

....

....

....

....

....

....

....

....

....

....

....

....

....

....

....

....

....

....

....

....

Your Family

When we pause and ask questions about the people who came before us, we begin understanding ourselves differently.

Do you find it hard to let go of things because your grandmother was raised in a home where every morsel had to last? Does your anxiety trace to ancestors who lived through horrific conditions, planting hyper-vigilance into your DNA? Do you love painting because your grandfather was always in the best mood at his easel? As you answer questions on the following pages, connections like these may begin to arise. If you don't know much or have anyone to ask, dig through genealogy sites or even history books—read about the places your parents, grandparents, and long-ago ancestors lived. What information can you find?

You did not arrive to this moment in time alone: you are a descendant of everyone who came before you, however unfamiliar and imperfect. The healing you are doing in this lifetime is not yours alone either—it is rippling backward and forward in time, sewing up long ago wounds and creating new pathways for the future. As you write about the mysteries of your ancestral lines on the following pages, continually ask yourself: *how can I compost this information for my own connection, healing, and freedom?*

A guided meditation and breathwork track to accompany this section can be found at FollowYourFireCoaching.com/yourself

What are the biggest lessons you learned from your mother?

....

....

....

....

....

....

....

....

....

....

....

....

What are some things she did that you're grateful for? What are some things that you wish she'd done differently?

....

....

....

....

....

....

....

....

....

....

....

....

....

What are the biggest lessons you learned from your father?

....
....
....
....
....
....
....
....
....
....
....

What are some things he did that you're grateful for? What are some things that you wish he'd done differently?

....
....
....
....
....
....
....
....
....
....
....
....

Is there anyone now gone from your family that you wish you'd been closer with? Why? ....
....
....
....
....
....
....
....
....
....
....

Is there anyone in your family that you'd currently like to be closer with? How can you foster more connection with them?
....
....
....
....
....
....
....
....
....
....
....
....
....

What were your grandparents' names? What words come to mind when you think of each one? ....

....

....

....

....

....

....

....

....

....

....

What things did you learn from them, whether through experience or stories others shared? ....

....

....

....

....

....

....

....

....

....

....

....

....

What do you know about how your grandparents on your mom's side grew up? Where did they live, what time frame were they raised in, and what major cultural events did they experience? ....

....

....

....

....

....

....

....

....

....

....

....

....

....

How do you think these circumstances shaped who they later became? ....

....

....

....

....

....

....

....

....

What do you know about how your grandparents on your dad's side grew up? Where did they live, what time frame were they raised in, and what major cultural events did they experience? ....

....

....

....

....

....

....

....

....

....

....

....

....

How do you think these circumstances shaped who they later became? ....

....

....

....

....

....

....

....

Where was your mother's immediate (and more distant) family from? Do you remember any stories they told about that place?

....
....
....
....
....
....
....
....
....
....

Where was your father's immediate (and more distant) family from? Do you remember any stories they told about that place?

....
....
....
....
....
....
....
....
....
....
....
....
....
....
....

How do you think your mother's relationship to her parents and upbringing shaped who she was? How do you think it shaped the way she parented? ....

....

....

....

....

....

....

....

....

....

How do you think your father's relationship to his parents and upbringing shaped who he was? How do you think it shaped the way he parented? ....

....

....

....

....

....

....

....

....

....

....

....

....

Is there any family lore that was passed down to you through stories? Maybe you had a famous ancestor, or mysterious family scandal? (This can be one to ask your elders if you have any, and much can be found on genealogy websites.)

....
....
....
....
....
....
....
....
....
....
....
....
....
....
....
....
....
....
....
....
....
....
....
....

Are there any common threads you notice throughout the limbs of your family tree? Certain talents, addictions, or mannerisms? It can help to consider how you would finish these sentences:

My mom's family were people who ....
....
....
....
....
....
....
....
....
....
....
....

My dad's family were people who ....
....
....
....
....
....
....
....
....
....
....

What is something you learned from the generations before you? ....

....

....

....

....

....

....

....

....

....

....

....

What was something that your parents found really important to teach you? Why do you think it was so important to them? ....

....

....

....

....

....

....

....

....

....

....

....

Are there any family cycles that you are intent on breaking?

....

....

....

....

....

....

....

....

....

....

....

....

What traditions or values do you hope to continue?

....

....

....

....

....

....

....

....

....

....

....

....

....

....

....

What new family cycles and stories are you weaving?

On Work

"First say to yourself what you would be,
and then do what you have to do."

~ Epictetus ~

Whether career is a pillar of your identity or a footnote in your story, the importance of work (even in its absence) is a thread in the tapestry of our lives. Mining your beliefs about work, identification with your career, and where you find purpose (both in the past and future) will help you understand why you've made the choices you have.

The questions on the following pages will give you a clearer understanding of where you've been, how it changed you, and where you're headed. The real "work" of reflecting on work is sweeping away all of the titles, roles, and identities—and finding the deeper beliefs beneath them.

A guided meditation and breathwork track to accompany this section can be found at FollowYourFireCoaching.com/yourself

When asked "what do you want to be when you grow up?" as a child, what did you say? ....

....

....

....

....

....

....

....

....

....

....

....

What jobs did you have when you were young? How did they shape who you later became? ....

....

....

....

....

....

....

....

....

....

....

....

....

....

How did your parents make a living? What about your grandparents? ....

....

....

....

....

....

....

....

....

....

....

....

What did your parents teach you about work? ....

....

....

....

....

....

....

....

....

....

....

....

....

....

Was there a job you always fantasized about but never did? Why was it so appealing? ....

....

....

....

....

....

....

....

....

....

....

....

Is there a job you think you'd be great at (or one others have always encouraged you to do) but doesn't interest you?

....

....

....

....

....

....

....

....

....

....

....

....

....

What was your *least* favorite job? Why? ....

....

....

....

....

....

....

....

....

....

....

....

What was your favorite job? Why? ....

....

....

....

....

....

....

....

....

....

....

....

....

....

....

How important is your career identity to you? ....
....
....
....
....
....
....
....
....
....
....
....

Were there any coworkers you especially loved working with? What qualities did you appreciate about them?

....
....
....
....
....
....
....
....
....
....
....
....

Do you believe work should simply be a means to an end, or also provide purpose and meaning? Do you identify somewhere in the middle? How have both ideas shown up in your life and career choices? ....

....

....

....

....

....

....

....

....

....

....

....

....

....

....

....

....

....

....

....

....

....

....

Are you happy with your career choices? Is there anything you would do differently if given the chance? ....

....
....
....
....
....
....
....
....
....
....
....
....
....
....
....
....
....
....
....
....
....
....
....
....
....

What part has having a family (or not) played into your work choices? ....

....

....

....

....

....

....

....

....

....

....

How do you define career success? How has your definition changed throughout time? ....

....

....

....

....

....

....

....

....

....

....

....

....

....

What career advice would you give your younger self?

....
....
....
....
....
....
....
....
....
....
....
....
....
....
....
....
....
....
....
....
....
....
....
....
....
....
....

Describe your ideal job, knowing what you know now.

....

....

....

....

....

....

....

....

....

....

....

....

....

....

....

....

....

....

....

....

....

....

....

....

....

Imagine yourself at eighty. What career advice do you think that future self would give you? ....

....

....

....

....

....

....

....

....

....

....

....

....

....

....

....

....

....

....

....

....

....

....

....

....

....

Your Relationships

"I am, because we are."

~ African Proverb ~

Whether it's friendship, romantic partnership, or family and friends, we are social animals that exist in relationships.

Understanding who we've gravitated toward in the past can explain certain patterns, preferences, and traits we have today. Noticing who leaves us feeling drained or energized in the present can help us navigate relationships with loving boundaries, clear communication, and grounded intention. We are who we are not from existing on an island, but because we are in constant dance with the people around us. Use the prompts on the following pages to move with more intention, joy, and understanding with each dance partner.

A guided meditation and breathwork track to accompany this section can be found at FollowYourFireCoaching.com/yourself

Do you remember your first date? What was it like?

....
....
....
....
....
....
....
....
....
....
....
....

Who was your first love? What words come to mind when
you think of them now? ....

....
....
....
....
....
....
....
....
....
....
....
....
....

What have you learned about yourself from being in love?

....
....
....
....
....
....
....
....
....
....
....

What have you learned from heartbreak? ....

....
....
....
....
....
....
....
....
....
....
....
....

Was there someone you thought you would end up with but didn't? If you could hand yourself a note just before that relationship ended, what would it say? ....

....

....

....

....

....

....

....

....

....

....

....

....

....

....

....

....

....

....

....

....

....

....

....

....

What do you believe are the most important qualities in a partner? ....
....
....
....
....
....
....
....
....
....
....

Whether coupled or single, do you feel that you are demonstrating those qualities yourself? ....
....
....
....
....
....
....
....
....
....
....
....
....

What advice would you give your younger self about romantic relationships?

....

....

....

....

....

....

....

....

....

....

....

....

....

....

....

....

....

....

....

....

....

....

....

....

....

What advice do you think your future self would give present-day you about romantic relationships? ....

....
....
....
....
....
....
....
....
....
....
....
....
....
....
....
....
....
....
....
....
....
....
....
....
....
....

How has your definition of an ideal partner or relationship changed over time? ....
....
....
....
....
....
....
....
....
....
....

If you could wipe your memory clean of an entire relationship, would you do it? Why or why not? ....
....
....
....
....
....
....
....
....
....
....
....
....

Who are your longest lasting friendships? What allowed these relationships to bridge gaps in time and circumstance?

....
....
....
....
....
....
....
....
....
....

Is there an important friend you're no longer close with? Was this friendship ended intentionally or by circumstance? What role do you think you played in each other's lives?

....
....
....
....
....
....
....
....
....
....
....
....
....

What do you consider the most important qualities in a friend? ....

....

....

....

....

....

....

....

....

....

....

....

Do you feel that you are demonstrating those qualities yourself? ....

....

....

....

....

....

....

....

....

....

....

....

....

....

If you could give your thirteen-year-old self advice about friendship, what would you tell them? ....

....

....

....

....

....

....

....

....

....

....

....

....

....

....

....

....

....

....

....

....

....

....

....

....

....

Who are the five people closest to you? List your favorite qualities about each one. Then text, call, or email these people and tell them. At a later date, consider asking them "what are your favorite qualities about me?" If you need a reason, say that you're filling out this journal or doing a self-understanding profile. Write their responses in here, and reread them whenever you need a boost.

My favorite qualities about five people: ....

....

....

....

....

....

....

....

....

....

Other people's favorite qualities about me: ....

....

....

....

....

....

....

....

....

....

Who can you always turn to when you need support? If you struggle with this list, consider: who would *I like* to lean on for support? How can I prioritize these relationships?

....
....
....
....
....
....
....
....
....
....
....
....
....
....
....
....
....
....
....
....
....
....
....
....

Who in your life leaves you feeling really energized? How can you prioritize these relationships? ....

....

....

....

....

....

....

....

....

....

....

....

Who leaves you feeling drained? How can you create boundaries around these relationships? ....

....

....

....

....

....

....

....

....

....

....

....

....

....

Whether they're presently in your life or long gone, bring to mind someone who believed wholeheartedly in you and your goodness. Maybe it was a parent, teacher, or treasured friend—just pause to remember how it felt to be in their presence. Write down the sort of things they believed about you. How can you let that inform the people you choose to have in your life today? ....

....

....

....

....

....

....

....

....

....

....

....

....

....

....

....

....

....

....

....

....

What role do you believe you play within your family? For example: are you the manager, caretaker, black sheep, organizer? What are the benefits to this role, and what are the drawbacks? ....

....

....

....

....

....

....

....

....

Is there anything you'd like to change about how you currently show up within your family role? For example, "I'd like to accept more help" or "I'd like to believe that I am valued just as I am, and not because of how I perform."

....

....

....

....

....

....

....

....

....

....

....

If you had a family mission statement, what would it be? What values are most important? If you feel stuck here, finish the sentence "we are people who .... each other" over and over. When you're done, consider talking to other family members about it, and putting it up somewhere you see often.

....

....

....

....

....

....

....

....

It's been said that relationships can magnify the places we are still the most in need of healing. What are some places of healing that come up for you in a relationship? How can you bring more love and less judgment to those parts?

....

....

....

....

....

....

....

....

....

....

....

What relationships have most changed you as a person? Why? ....
....
....
....
....
....
....
....
....
....
....
....
....
....
....
....
....
....
....
....
....
....
....
....
....
....
....

Something Bigger

The idea of "Something Bigger" means different things to different people.

Maybe words like God, Spiritual, or Higher Power feel great for you, or maybe you're repelled by them. Maybe you're a devoted practitioner with a rich spiritual life, or maybe you're unsure if there's something "Higher" at all, choosing instead to avoid using any of these words. As a reflective person filling out a journal like this one, you've likely felt shifting beliefs at different points in your life, which is a gift. That open-minded part of you is the liminal space from which to write.

May this combination of willingness, openness, and writing bring you into a dance with mystery on the pages that follow, shifting and swaying with a larger choreographer that connects you to Life Itself.

A guided meditation and breathwork track to accompany this section can be found at FollowYourFireCoaching.com/yourself

Did you have a relationship with God or a Higher Power in childhood? How did you form it? ....

....

....

....

....

....

....

....

....

....

....

Did your family have any religious traditions? If so, do you still practice them? Why or why not? ....

....

....

....

....

....

....

....

....

....

....

....

....

....

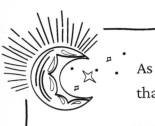

As a child, what was your idea of God? How does that compare to your idea of a Higher Power today?

Childhood

....
....
....
....
....
....
....
....
....
....
....
....
....
....
....
....
....
....
....
....
....
....
....
....

Today

....
....
....
....
....
....
....
....
....
....
....
....
....
....
....
....
....
....
....
....
....
....
....
....

Have you had any spiritual experiences that are especially sacred to you? ....
....
....
....
....
....
....
....
....
....
....
....
....
....
....
....
....
....
....
....
....
....
....
....
....
....
....

Where do you connect the most with your spirituality? If you don't identify as spiritual, where do you feel the most connected to the greater forces at work in the world?

....

....

....

....

....

....

....

....

....

When did you last experience the feeling of awe? Was it beneath the vast starry sky, beside crashing waves at the ocean, witnessing the birth of a child? Bring to mind this experience and write about it in detail. Conjure the way it felt in that moment and return to it when you are in need of calm, comfort, or connection. ....

....

....

....

....

....

....

....

....

....

What do you do when you've lost faith? ....
....
....
....
....
....
....
....
....
....
....
....

Have you had any otherworldly experiences that stayed
with you? ....
....
....
....
....
....
....
....
....
....
....
....
....
....

Knowing Yourself
Better

If someone were to ask you what experiences made you who you are, you'd probably share some of the big moments: the family you were born into, career choices you made, and the positive or negative experiences that got you here. But the truth is that you're also composed of many important smaller parts: granular snapshots, memories, and preferences that make up the soil from which you currently bloom.

Consider this section like getting to know a new friend: someone you barely know but find fascinating, a person who seems more endearing, familiar, and good with every new thing you learn about them. That new friend is you—but from a different angle.

Use the prompts on the following pages to understand this friend on a level that brings more compassion, integration, and wholeness. They've been waiting to meet you for a while.

A guided meditation and breathwork track to accompany this section can be found at FollowYourFireCoaching.com/yourself

What is a concert you'll never forget? Why was it so memorable?

....
....
....
....
....
....
....
....

What is your favorite meal? What does it remind you of?

....
....
....
....
....
....
....
....

What are some of your favorite smells? What do they remind
you of? ....
....
....
....
....
....
....
....

What are some of your favorite books and movies? Why do you love them? ....
....
....
....
....
....
....

Where are some of the places you have lived in life? Which was your favorite? Why? ....
....
....
....
....
....
....

What are you insecure about? Do you know where this came from? How do you navigate this and show up anyway?
....
....
....
....
....
....
....

If you won the lottery tomorrow, what are the first things you'd do with it? ....

....

....

....

....

....

....

How can your answer point you toward where to spend your time and energy today? (For example, for whom would you buy a new house, what charity would you support, and how would you modify your current circumstances? These are all arrows toward your values and can help you prioritize your present-day life.) ....

....

....

....

....

....

....

How much money is "enough?" What does enough money feel like? ....

....

....

....

....

....

What are your favorite qualities about yourself? ....

....

....

....

....

....

....

....

....

....

....

....

....

Is there something that people often get wrong about you?

....

....

....

....

....

....

....

....

....

....

....

....

....

....

....

Are there any momentous days or cultural events that you'll never forget? How did they affect you? ....

....

....

....

....

....

....

....

....

....

....

What is something you've changed your mind about?

....

....

....

....

....

....

....

....

....

....

....

....

....

....

You're given the chance to relive one day of your life. Which one is it? Why? ....

....

....

....

....

....

....

....

....

....

What will you never do again? ....

....

....

....

....

....

....

....

....

....

....

....

....

....

What is one dream you've let go of? Where do you still see it show up in your life? ....

....

....

....

....

....

....

....

....

....

What is something you always want to talk about but no one ever asks you to? ....

....

....

....

....

....

....

....

....

....

....

....

....

What are ten things that, when you do them, feel like you're taking really good care of yourself? (e.g: flossing your teeth, calling a friend, savoring a yummy food slowly, etc.)

....

....

....

....

....

....

....

....

....

....

....

....

....

....

....

....

....

....

....

....

....

....

....

How can you incorporate these things into your days more often?

Integrating Self

We all contain varying parts of self. Some of these parts we're happy to be known for (like being funny, responsible, or intelligent) and others we'd rather not identify with (like being controlling, flaky, or judge-mental.) The truth for all of us is that many (often conflicting) parts are present at different times. Rather than overly identifying with the "good," and judging or trying to eliminate the "bad," we can instead name, welcome, and integrate them all.

Get to know your *unwanted* identities by finishing the following sentences

I *don't* want to be known as someone who is: ......*quality one*......

If I'm perceived as .....*quality one*....., I'm afraid that: ....

....

....

....

If this identity is viewed from a lens of love: *(Is it here to protect you? Are there benefits to this identity? Is it possible to be loved even when you are portraying this trait?)* ....

....

....

....

....

I *don't* want to be known as someone who is: ......*quality two*......
If I'm perceived as ....*quality two*...., I'm afraid that: ....

....

....

....

If this identity is viewed from a lens of love: *(Is it here to protect you? Are there benefits to this identity? Is it possible to be loved even when you are portraying this trait?)* ....

....

....

....

....

I *don't* want to be known as someone who is: ......*quality three*......
If I'm perceived as ....*quality three*...., I'm afraid that: ....

....

....

....

If this identity is viewed from a lens of love: *(Is it here to protect you? Are there benefits to this identity? Is it possible to be loved even when you are portraying this trait?)* ....

....

....

....

....

Get to know your *wanted* identities by finishing the following sentences

I *want* to be known as someone who is: ....*quality one*........

Why I view this as a positive trait: ....

....

....

....

Where I see this identity show up the most frequently: (With whom? Doing what?) ....

....

....

....

I *want* to be known as someone who is: ....*quality two*........

Why I view this as a positive trait: ....

....

....

....

Where I see this identity show up the most frequently: (With whom? Doing what?) ....

....

....

....

I *want* to be known as someone who is: ....*quality three*.......

Why I view this as a positive trait: ....

....

....

Where I see this identity show up the most frequently:

(With whom? Doing what?) ....

....

....

....

I *want* to be known as someone who is: ....*quality four*.......

Why I view this as a positive trait: ....

....

....

Where I see this identity show up the most frequently:

(With whom? Doing what?) ....

....

....

....

When we realize that all of these identities orbit a deeper Self, we can feel less shame about our unwanted parts, less attachment to other people's perception of us, and more compassion overall. After filling this section out, integrate what you've found by practicing the "Calling in all parts" meditation found at FollowYourFireCoaching.com/callinginallparts

What is something that always makes you smile?

....

....

....

....

....

....

....

....

What is an ordinary moment from your day that makes you feel extremely grateful? ....

....

....

....

....

....

....

....

Where are your favorite places to travel? Why?

....

....

....

....

....

....

....

Are there any points in your life that you completely changed course? How did they change you? ....

....

....

....

....

....

....

What are people often surprised to learn about you?

....

....

....

....

....

....

....

Are there any songs that always make you feel better? After making the list, consider making them into a playlist that you can turn to when you need a boost. ....

....

....

....

....

....

....

What do you want to spend more time doing? What do you want to waste less time doing? ....
....
....
....
....
....
....
....

What is something you learned later in life that you wish you'd learned earlier? ....
....
....
....
....
....
....
....

What is your favorite aspect of your present-day body? Have you always loved this part? ....
....
....
....
....
....
....
....

Is the present anything like you imagined the future would be when you were a kid? How is it different or the same? ....

....

....

....

....

....

....

What are some of your favorite quotes? ....

....

....

....

....

....

....

....

What do you believe are important keys to living a good life?

....

....

....

....

....

....

....

....

....

What are some things that you think everyone should experience in life? Why? ....

....

....

....

....

....

....

....

....

....

....

....

....

....

....

....

....

....

....

....

....

....

....

....

....

....

Identifying Your Values

We make choices everyday that get us closer or further to the life we want to lead. Beneath these choices are our values—the things we hold most dear and are willing to prioritize. If we don't spend time getting clear on which values are most important, we can end up living out of alignment by accidentally prioritizing the wrong things. The following section will help you identify the core values that you want driving your daily choices.

Keep in mind that these values will change over time: what is important to you now probably wasn't twenty years ago, and what might be important in twenty more years isn't right now. For this reason, returning to this exercise again and again (some do a values check on a yearly basis) can help realign you when you're feeling off.

A guided meditation and breathwork track to accompany this section can be found at FollowYourFireCoaching.com/yourself

Finding Your Core Values

From the list of values below, circle the 12–15 that feel
most important. Feel free to add any not included in the
list. After circling those, move onto the next page.

Accomplishment	Comfort	Ease
Accountability	Commitment	Effectiveness
Adventure	Community	Energy
Altruism	Compassion	Education
Ambition	Confidence	Enjoyment
Appearance	Connection	Expansion
Authenticity	Consistency	Exploration
Balance	Contribution	Family
Beauty	Control	Fairness
Calm	Creativity	Fame
Career	Curiosity	Flexibility
Cleanliness	Dependability	Freedom
Challenge	Devotion	Friendship

Fun	Perseverance	Spontaneity
Generosity	Predictability	Stability
Growth	Presence	Status
Happiness	Productivity	Strength
Health	Purpose	Sustainability
Honesty	Recognition	Tradition
Influence	Relationships	Truth
Integrity	Reliability	Trustworthiness
Innovation	Resilience	Wealth
Love	Responsibility	Wonder
Kindness	Respect	....
Mastery	Romance	....
Meaning	Security	....
Movement	Service	....
Nature	Simplicity	....
Peace	Spirituality	....

Now flip back to the previous page and narrow down to 3–5 values that feel most important. Write them in the space below—these are your present core values.

My core values are:

....
    value one   *value two*   *value three*

Now that you've identified your core values, how are you living them? In the space below, write out the values that you circled on the previous page. Next to each one, explain how these values are lived through action. For example, if a core value is love, where are you demonstrating love in your life? If a core value is family, how are you living in alignment with that? If you struggle to see clear examples or notice any discrepancies, be gentle with yourself. Through a combination of culture, conditioning, and the individual patterns each of us fall into, most of us experience gaps between the values we hold and the unconscious way we have learned to live our lives. Which is exactly why we do exercises like this—to bring our lives into alignment.

Where can I bring more ....*value one*........................ into my life?

....

....

Where can I bring more ....*value two*........................ into my life?

....

....

Where can I bring more ....*value three*........................ into my life?

....

....

Navigating Tough Moments

Most of us would not choose pain. We wouldn't ask to go through horrific breakups, face health issues, or watch the people and animals close to us die. We'd turn left instead of right to avoid the accidents, trap doors, and the moments that might have put us in a state of hyper-vigilance for years afterward. These painful parts of life, however expected or common, are the hardest part of our journey being human. And yet, being fully here for our lives means facing the pain too. Understanding how our present-day selves were affected by difficult moments can help us see them through a different lens: one of meaning alongside the unfairness, and wisdom alongside the grief.

Use the questions on the following pages to better understand how the difficulties you've faced have changed you as a person—mine them for the gifts, experience, and meaning that you get to create yourself.

Knowing that we wouldn't have chosen these difficulties can coexist with another important truth: going through them made us who we are today. That's someone with more awareness of life's precarity, and who has allowed the cracks in our certainty to make way for more light in the present. Onward.

A guided meditation and breathwork track to accompany this section can be found at FollowYourFireCoaching.com/yourself

What is one of the toughest decisions you've ever had to make? Did you struggle with the path not taken? ....

....
....
....
....
....
....
....
....
....
....
....
....
....
....
....
....
....
....
....
....
....
....
....
....
....
....
....

Would you make the same choice today? If not, how can you bring compassion to the version of you that was doing the best they could? ....

....

....

....

....

....

....

....

....

....

....

....

....

....

....

....

....

....

....

....

....

....

....

....

What advice would you give someone who is confused, feeling stuck, and overwhelmed? How would you help them decide which next step to take? ....

....

....

....

....

....

....

....

....

....

....

....

....

....

....

....

....

....

....

....

....

....

....

....

....

Do you believe that everything happens for a reason? If so, reflect on an experience where this has been true for you. If not, how have you "made meaning" from the things that have happened to you? ....

....

....

....

....

....

....

....

....

....

....

....

....

....

....

....

....

....

....

....

....

....

....

....

....

....

What is one of your most difficult experiences? How did it change you? ....

....
....
....
....
....
....
....
....
....
....
....
....
....
....
....
....
....
....
....
....
....
....
....
....
....
....

If you could hand yourself a note before facing that difficult experience, what would it say? ....

....

....

....

....

....

....

....

....

....

....

....

....

....

....

....

....

....

....

....

....

....

....

....

....

Was there a particularly challenging season of your life? How did you cope during that time? ....

....
....
....
....
....
....
....
....
....
....
....
....
....
....
....
....
....
....
....
....
....
....
....
....
....

Did anyone offer much needed (or even unexpected) support to you during that period? ....
....
....
....
....
....
....
....
....
....
....
....

Who have you supported through a difficult time? How did it feel to be that support? ....
....
....
....
....
....
....
....
....
....
....
....
....
....
....

Is there anything (or anyone) you were forced to give up, but wouldn't have chosen to? How did you handle that?

....
....
....
....
....
....
....
....
....
....
....

What is the first thing you do when you are really afraid?

....
....
....
....
....
....
....
....
....
....
....
....
....
....
....
....

Think back to ten years ago. What would have been your biggest problems during that time? How do they compare to your problems today? ....

....

....

....

....

....

....

....

....

....

....

....

....

....

....

....

....

....

....

....

....

....

....

....

....

....

What "quality problems" do you have today? These are struggles in circumstances that your former self might have been surprised or even happy to have. E.g: struggles with parenting *(we have kids now?)*, to pay your mortgage *(we bought a house?)*, or with aging *(we get to grow old?)* This isn't to minimize the true difficulties of your present day, but to remember when circumstances like these were only a dream for you. ....

....

....

....

....

....

....

....

....

....

....

....

....

....

....

....

....

....

....

....

....

What things brought you comfort in times of difficulty as a child? Did you turn to certain books, settings, or activities? Even if it seems silly, consider incorporating these tools back into your present day when you need a lift.

....

....

....

....

....

....

....

....

....

....

....

....

....

....

....

....

....

....

....

....

....

....

....

....

....

What was a difficult goodbye of your life? How did it change you? ....

....

....

....

....

....

....

....

....

....

....

....

....

....

....

....

....

....

....

....

....

....

....

....

....

....

....

Is there anyone whose death greatly affected you, even if you didn't know them well? Why do you think this person made such an impact? ....

....

....

....

....

....

....

....

....

....

....

....

....

....

....

....

....

....

....

....

....

....

....

....

....

How would you tell someone to "let go" when it's time for a change? What does letting go feel like? ....

....

....

....

....

....

....

....

....

....

....

....

....

....

....

....

....

....

....

....

....

....

....

....

....

....

How does letting go differ from giving up? ....

....

....

....

....

....

....

....

....

....

....

....

....

....

....

....

....

....

....

....

....

....

....

....

....

....

....

....

Is there a difficult experience that you are now extremely grateful for? ....

....

....

....

....

....

....

....

....

....

....

....

....

....

....

....

....

....

....

....

....

....

....

....

....

....

What words would you share with someone who thought that they were insignificant, or that their life didn't have meaning? ....

....

....

....

....

....

....

....

....

....

....

....

....

....

....

....

....

....

....

....

....

....

....

....

....

....

What are some things that have always brought you comfort during difficulty? *Use this list as a "care kit" later—one that can serve as comfort during your next difficult season.*

....
....
....
....
....
....
....
....
....
....
....
....
....
....
....
....
....
....
....
....
....
....
....
....
....
....

Your Future Self

Thinking about the future can change us in the present.

We realize that one day the pile of dirty laundry in front of us will be a relic from a bygone era—that the difficult conversation we're facing will be a blip on the arc of our life story. We can't live from fifty thousand feet up all the time, but taking moments to venture that high can help us see where we're going, decide if we want to change course, and be intentional creators of our present-day lives.

The following questions invite you to step into a time machine: one where you get to meet your future self, wise inner elder, and the person lovingly inviting you to consider: "how will we want to have lived?"

Much like the oak was always present in the acorn, your future self is already here and inevitable. Rather than being anxious when considering this self, trust that future you has your back and knows that you're doing the best you can today. May they show you the gifts of considering the future, as well as those already laid at your feet: present-day you.

A guided meditation and breathwork track to accompany this section can be found at FollowYourFireCoaching.com/yourself

Imagine yourself at eighty. Where are you living? What sort of clothes do you wear? Who do you see regularly? Allow yourself to make this your ideal vision, rather than sink into fearful possibilities. How is your healthiest, wisest, and most authentic inner eighty-year-old living? ....

....

....

....

....

....

....

....

....

....

....

....

....

....

....

....

....

....

....

....

....

....

....

What would that inner eighty-year-old want you to know today? ....
....
....
....
....
....
....
....
....
....
....

Consider a decision that you're facing in the present day. Then consider that inner elder you've just accessed. How might they advise you? ....
....
....
....
....
....
....
....
....
....
....

A question to consider weekly, monthly, yearly

At the end of this ....(week / month / year)........ *how do I want to feel?*
What things can I do today to guide me to that feeling?

....
....
....
....
....

At the end of this ....(week / month / year)........ *how do I want to feel?*
What things can I do today to guide me to that feeling?

....
....
....
....
....

At the end of this ....(week / month / year)........ *how do I want to feel?*
What things can I do today to guide me to that feeling?

....
....
....
....
....

At the end of life, what do you think will have been most important to you? ....

....

....

....

....

....

....

....

....

....

....

How can you prioritize these things or people more today?

....

....

....

....

....

....

....

....

....

....

....

....

....

....

Is there any part of your body you think you'll wish you had taken more care of? How can you take better care of it today?

....

....

....

....

....

....

....

....

....

....

What hopes do you have for our world in the next twenty years? Are there any changes you want to be a part of? Without taking on the "weight of the world," how can you take one step toward these changes today? ....

....

....

....

....

....

....

....

....

....

....

If you could meet your great-great-grandparents, what would you want to ask them? What questions would they have for you? Consider for a moment the time they lived through, the things they faced, the children they raised. ....

....

....

....

....

....

....

....

....

If you were to meet your adult great-great-grandchildren, what qualities would you hope they possess? What sort of a world would you imagine for them? (If you don't have or plan to have children, imagine the grown children from two generations ahead.) ....

....

....

....

....

....

....

....

....

....

Thirty years into the future, what do you think you will care the most about? Does that change anything about your priorities today? ....

....

....

....

....

....

....

....

....

....

How has your definition of a successful life changed over time? ....

....

....

....

....

....

....

....

....

....

....

....

....

What things do you want to experience before you die?
Jot down what comes to mind in the space below, and
remember that you can always keep adding to this list.

....
....
....
....
....
....
....
....
....
....
....
....
....
....
....
....
....
....
....
....
....
....
....
....
....
....
....

You travel through time and eavesdrop on your funeral. What do you hope to overhear? ....

....

....

....

....

....

....

....

....

....

....

....

....

....

....

....

....

....

....

....

....

....

....

....

....

What would your future self say you spent too much time doing? ....

....

....

....

....

....

....

....

....

....

....

What would they say you didn't spend enough time doing?

....

....

....

....

....

....

....

....

....

....

....

....

....

....

....

Being human is a wild ride. There are incredible things, like taking warm baths and seeing shooting stars, and there are terrible things, like hearing nails on a chalkboard or losing a treasured pet. Imagine that you're going to leave your human body soon, and make a list of the things you'll miss and the things you won't. What's on it?

Things I'll miss	*Things I won't*
....	....
....	....
....	....
....	....
....	....
....	....
....	....
....	....
....	....
....	....
....	....
....	....
....	....
....	....
....	....
....	....
....	....
....	....
....	....

What do you think happens when we die? What do you hope happens? ....

....

....

....

....

....

....

....

....

....

....

....

....

....

....

....

....

....

....

....

....

....

....

....

....

....

When you are gone, how do you hope to be remembered?

....
....
....
....
....
....
....
....
....
....
....
....
....
....
....
....
....
....
....
....
....
....
....
....
....
....

If you could choose your last words, what would they be?

....
....
....
....
....
....
....
....
....
....
....
....
....
....
....
....
....
....
....
....
....
....
....
....
....
....

What ending was also a beginning for you? ....
....
....
....
....
....
....
....
....
....
....
....
....
....
....
....
....
....
....
....
....
....
....
....
....
....

Questions for Every Day

Every day we make large and small choices that construct a larger mosaic of our lives. Rather than letting this truth pressure us to do something big, important, or outwardly measurable, it can remind us that each day is a new chance to show up the way we want.

Do I want to live with more love, compassion, trust? Do I have a goal that feels good and right, one that I want to keep in focus as I navigate my day? Do I want to center a specific word, feeling, or intention?

You've always got a new chance, right here, on this day. Let the questions in the following section be daily guides toward the life you desire. This section of the journal has no space to write because these inquiries are meant to be returned to again and again—use them in your personal journal as a daily writing practice, program them into your phone as a daily calendar reminder, or put up a few in your home in a place that you see often.

A daily reminder: the life you seek is not "out there" waiting for you to achieve a certain goal, body, or status level. It is always right here at your feet, ready to be remembered and lived from the exact place you are standing right now. Sometimes it just takes asking the right question.

A guided meditation and breathwork track to accompany this section can be found at FollowYourFireCoaching.com/yourself

Here are some suggestions for when in your day to ask these questions, but remember that there's no "wrong" time; it's never too late to start (or restart) your day.

QUESTIONS FOR THE BEGINNING OF YOUR DAY

What is my intention today?

What is my biggest priority or goal today?

If it would help to have accountability around this goal, who can I ask to check in with later today?

If I could only get one thing done today, what would it be?

If I could choose a word to anchor me today, what would it be?

Some examples: power, sacred, truth, beauty, connection, flow, grounded, peaceful, rest, healing, ease, expand

What do I want to be, feel, and do today?

Is there anyone I've been longing to connect with or reach out to? How can I do so today?

What five dreams do I have today?
(These can be long-term, large or small, and do not have to be attained today—writing down five dreams daily can help grow your space of possibility.)

How can I help someone, contribute, or be of service today?

How do I want to show up to my day?
(Take a moment to envision your day's plans and see yourself acting, feeling, and being who you most desire.)

What am I grateful for? Who am I grateful for? How can I practice gratitude through my actions today?

How can I make today sacred?

Are the things I am doing today getting me closer to or farther from the life I want?

At the end of the day, what will I most wish to have done or felt?

QUESTIONS FOR THE END OF YOUR DAY

What did I learn today?

What was beautiful today?

Who made my day better?
(Consider reaching out to tell them)

What was difficult about today?

If I could change something about my actions today,
what would it be? How can I let that inform how
I show up tomorrow?

Is there anyone I feel uneasy with, whom I want
to reach out to in order to clear the air?
*(You don't have to do so right away; take time to journal
or breathe into this. Consider calling someone to talk it
over first. Then, when you're ready to reach out, invite love
to join the conversation—see the interaction surrounded
by support, ease, and light.)*

How would my day be different if I looked
at it through the eyes of compassion,
innocence, and love?

What am I proud of myself for doing, being,
or feeling today?

What am I grateful for about today?
What am I grateful for in general?

Where or how do I want to act
differently tomorrow?

Where can I be more loving to myself
or another tomorrow?

What was the best part of my day?

What guidance do I want to ask for
in my dreams tonight?

What questions have you found helpful to ask yourself on a daily basis? Fill in your favorites below. ....

....

....

....

....

....

....

....

....

....

....

....

....

....

....

....

....

....

....

....

....

....

....

....

....

....

Questions for the Liminal Space

Sometimes we need to ask questions that don't have clean answers: inquiries that lead us out of the cerebral headspace of thinking, and into our heartspace of intuitive knowing.

Turn to the questions in the following section when you're in need of guidance, clarity, calm, or support. Rather than journaling your answers outright, consider connecting them to a practice that opens your heart and integrates your body. This looks like asking a question and then sitting in meditation, doing a breathwork practice, taking a long walk, or practicing another type of accessible movement session. After this adjoining practice, sit down with a notebook and do some stream of consciousness writing with your answer. For support doing this on a regular basis, join the Living Questions & Breathing Answers group at FollowYourFireCoaching.com/Yourself (for more information about this group see page 157.)

There is so much wisdom within. When we unhook from needing the exact answers, our inner guide has a chance to come through. Make way for that guide on the following pages.

A guided meditation and breathwork track to accompany this section can be found at FollowYourFireCoaching.com/yourself

What do I most need to know right now?

What am I trying to not know?

Where do I feel out of balance?

Where am I most in need of support?

What would support feel like right now?

What do I want more of?

What do I want less of?

Where do I need space right now?

What is the next right thing?

How would things be different if
I didn't need to know?

What if I trusted more?

If my health or body is sending a signal,
what is it saying?

Where is the line between acceptance
and resignation?

What would radical acceptance feel like?

What guides can I call in for support
right now?

If there was no wrong path,
what would I choose?

How would this situation be different if
viewed through a lens of compassion,
innocence, and love?

What is here for me right now?

Love Notes
from Myself

Use the following blank pages to jot down any notes that feel important, ideas you want to contemplate further, or answers that didn't fit elsewhere.

....
....
....
....
....
....
....
....
....
....
....
....
....
....
....
....
....

Afterword

Regardless of how you approached this journal, I hope you found someone very special within its pages... You.

You at many ages and stages, you in the past and future, you at your most shadowy and you at your most vibrant. I hope that journeying to all of these versions of self was a reminder that they orbit a deeper one—a Self that is unchanging, whole, and possesses a deeper knowing. I urge you to return to these questions again and again: whether you write your new answers in fraying spiral notebooks or on the back of airplane napkins, just keep returning. After all, it was never about holding onto the pretty answers—it was about being brave enough to live the questions, over and over and over again. If you want to deepen this practice and do so in an open-hearted community, you can join us in the Living Questions and Breathing Answers group at FollowyourfireCoaching.com. There you'll find more questions, a library of recorded meditations and breathwork practices, and live breathwork ceremonies and journaling sessions. All are welcome, and all of you is welcome.

As you move forward, may you stay willing, open, and keep a beginner's mind, even with yourself. Dare to live in the liminal space where nothing you've gone through is wasted, no part of your future needs agonizing, and the present moment is always the sacred ground of the next right thing. Dare to call in every part of you.

~Melissa Pennel

Mental Health Resources

Mental health is always important, and journeying within can be a tender endeavor. Consider accessing professional help to support you on this journey. Use the below resources as a starting point to accessing support locally. You are not alone and there is help.

SAMHSA
(Substance Abuse and Mental Health Services Administration)
Website: SAMHSA.gov
Phone: 1-800-662-HELP (4357)

NAMI
(National Alliance on Mental Illness)
Website: NAMI.org
Phone: 1-800-950-NAMI (6264)

NATIONAL SUICIDE PREVENTION LIFELINE
Website: suicidepreventionlifeline.org
Phone: 1-800-273-8255

Come Join Us in the Living Questions, Breathing Answers Group

For more support with this journal and on your healing journey in general, come join us in the Living Questions & Breathing Answers group at Followyourfirecoaching.com/yourself. You'll have access to over twenty guided meditations and breathwork practices (new tracks added monthly), additional journaling prompts and live journaling sessions where we'll all write together, and the option to attend monthly group breathwork ceremonies (as well as access to the replays to breathe on your own.)

About the Author

Melissa Pennel is a writer, mother, and author of the "Questions You'll Wish You Asked" series of journals. She facilitates the virtual "Living Questions, Breathing Answers" group at *FollowYourFireCoaching.com/yourself* and lives in Northern California with her partner, children, and beloved cats. To find more of Melissa's work on how to live a full and authentic life, go to

FollowYourFireCoaching.com

Made in the USA
Monee, IL
17 September 2023

42663739R00099